Dane Love is the author of numerous books on Scotland in general and on Ayrshire in
but now lives in the countryside near Auchinleck. He is descended from Robin Love, v
at the battles of Prestonpans and Culloden. A member of Ayrshire Archaeologic
he is also the Honorary Secretary of the Scottish Covenanter Memorials Associati
Antiquaries of Scotland. He works as a Principal Teacher at Irvine Royal Academy. I
around Scotland with his wife and two children, visiting historic sites

An Ayrshire Pattern Number 1 Harvest Cart, as made by A. Pollock in Mauchline.

Title Page and Back Cover: Jack & Sons of Maybole's 'New Empire Manure Distributor'.
Following Page: A green Fordson N tractor at Barmickhill farm, near Cumnock, c. 1950.
Jackie Kirkland is driving, with brothers James, Hugh and John getting a 'hurl'.

Fordson

A Look Back at AYRSHIRE FARMING

Dane Love

CARN PUBLISHING

First Published in Great Britain, 2011.

Reprinted 2013

ISBN – 978 0 9567550 2 5

Published by Carn Publishing,
Lochnoran House,
Auchinleck,
Ayrshire, KA18 3JW.

www.carnpublishing.com

Printed by Bell & Bain Ltd.,
Glasgow, G46 7UQ.

Introduction

Ayrshire is famed for its agricultural heritage. It also remains one of the most productive agricultural counties in Scotland, with a diversity that is unmatched in other parts of the country. Along the coast, in particular around Girvan and West Kilbride, the growing of potatoes has long been one of the main employers. The rolling fields behind this coastal strip for centuries have been home to dairy farms, and also to cattle breeding for beef. On the uplands that fringe the county, from the Largs heights in the north, through the Kyle hills and the Carrick uplands to the south, the grazing of sheep is important. In total, it is reckoned that there are 664,960 acres in the county.

Historically, farming in the county was carried out by cottars, who farmed small holdings, often as little as fifty acres in extent or less. In the eighteenth century the agricultural revolution saw many estates reallocate their lands, merging numerous small farms into larger units, and introducing enclosures, formed by planting hedges or building stone dikes. The number of workers needed on the land was reduced, many of those dispossessed finding new jobs as weavers in the villages that were created at the same time.

By the early nineteenth century, most farms in Ayrshire were still fairly small, measuring around 50-150 acres. As time passed, many of these farms were merged to form larger units, so that today some of the larger farms can be in excess of 500 acres in extent.

Agriculture has passed through a difficult time, when political interference has introduced quotas in milk production, reducing the number of dairy farmers in the county, a drop in sale prices for sheep and wool, and the transference of land near the towns for housing and golf-courses, or in the uplands for forestry. Grants have been introduced to improve the environment for wild animals, birds and insects, returning the woodland planting that formerly existed, or else 'set-aside' – fields left untouched and unproductive.

The brown and white Ayrshire cow is famous across the world for its excellent milk. They are thought to have been created by breeding Teeswater cattle with the local Cuninghame cow in the eighteenth century. In 1814 the Highland and Agricultural Society accepted it as a distinct breed. The Ayrshire Cattle Herd Book Society was founded in 1877 to record the pedigree of the cattle, and to ensure its protection. In more recent years, however, most dairy farmers in the county have changed to Friesian or Holstein cattle, and the true Ayrshire breed has been reduced in number.

Ayrshire cows are still to be found in other parts of the world, in places as diverse as Russia, Canada, Kenya and Finland, the latter country having the largest number of them. The cow is hardier than other breeds, and can produce good quality milk on poorer grassland. In recent years Ayrshire milk has become desirable once more, the supermarket Marks and Spencer paying a premium for it, which they sell under the Ayrshire milk label.

In 1949 it was reckoned that Ayrshire had 50,000 dairy cattle, producing one quarter of Scotland's total milk output. This milk was often treated on the farms and sold by small local dairies. Often, the larger farms or estates had a more commercial set-up, and milk was taken farther afield, such as to the markets of Glasgow.

Milk was also produced for making cheese, butter and dried milk. Creameries existed across the county, often in small works near to rivers, the waterwheels powering the machinery. The manufacture of cheese was at one time noted in the Dunlop area, Dunlop cheese being a famous form of hard cheese. It is said that it was first produced around 1700 at The Hill by Barbara Gilmour, who had brought the technique from Ireland. Using Ayrshire milk, the cheese became a successful variety that could withstand transport to the markets in the central belt and it would keep for some time. By the late nineteenth century this was replaced by 'Scotch Cheddar'. For many years until the twentieth century the largest cheese show in Scotland took place in Kilmarnock.

Creameries were established on a larger scale at Kilmarnock (Rowallan - 1888), Stewarton (early 1900s), Kilmaurs (1905), Kirkmichael (1908), Mauchline (1936), and at Waterside, near Fenwick. These took milk in bulk and either processed it for sale to more distant markets, such as Glasgow and Clydesdale, or else converted it into cheese, butter or margarine. Today, none of these creameries survives.

Beef cattle are also bred in the county, though on a smaller scale. However, with the over-production of milk, and the introduction of political quotas, many farmers have given up their dairies and instead concentrate on beef cattle and sheep.

The uplands and moors of the county are used for grazing sheep, usually the Blackface variety. These are a source of wool for weaving and milling, mutton for food and lambs for fattening. Other varieties bred in considerable number included the Border Leicester and Cheviot, usually on the lower farms.

The breeding of pigs for bacon was at one time popular in the county but this has basically died off. Some farms still have pigs however, but not on the scale that they once were.

The early Ayrshire potato is famed for its taste far beyond the county. The growing of potatoes did not become a large scale venture until after 1740, prior to that the vegetables were more or less just grown for local consumption. The potato was at one time brought on in boxes, the seed stored in trays above the byre or other building and once the sprouts had started to grow they were planted in the fields. The early crops were usually lifted about the end of June.

The manufacture of agricultural implements is one of Ayrshire's lost industries. Among well-known names that have disappeared include Hunter of Maybole which made ploughs, sowing machines, etc., MacCartney of Cumnock, which made threshing machines, Jack of Maybole which made ploughs and other implements, Dickie of Girvan, noted for their 'Scuffler' grubbers, patented in 1867, MacKerrow of Beansburn at Kilmarnock, and Begg of Dalry and Begg of Tarbolton, all of which made ploughs. In Ayr, Wallace Brothers were noted for their reaping machinery, and J. & T. Young made horse and steam threshing machines, many of which were exported to Ireland and the British colonies. In 1949 the Canadian firm of Massey Harris established a factory at Moorfield, on the edge of Kilmarnock, for the manufacture of tractors and combine harvesters. The company grew to employ about 1,500 workers, but with a drop in demand the firm (renamed Massey Ferguson) closed in February 1980.

Many farmers' societies and other organisations have been formed across the county, from self-improvement groups to specialist breeders. The Kilmarnock Farmers' Society was founded in 1792, the Ayrshire Agricultural Association by Sir James Fergusson, 4th Baronet of Kilkerran, in 1836. Most of the agricultural societies run their own annual shows, with competitions for cattle and produce as well as trade stands selling wares to customers. The largest of these is Ayr County Show, with smaller ones including Beith, Catrine, Colmonell & Ballantrae, Coylton, Craigie, Dalry, Dalrymple, Dundonald, Fenwick, Kilmaurs, Muirkirk, New Cumnock, Newmilns, Ochiltree, Straiton, Stewarton & Dunlop and Tarbolton.

The first milk-recording to take place in Scotland occured in 1903 at Fenwick, where 34 herds were involved. There were at one time twelve Young Farmers' Clubs in the county, but today only eight remain – Ayr, Beith, Carrick, Crossroads, Dunlop, Kilmaurs, Mauchline and New Cumnock.

Some old traditions have died away. One of the more common was the 'day's darg' given to new tenants. Leases historically were comparatively short, perhaps nine or eighteen years, and so farmers often moved from farm to farm. To mark their arrival at a new place, friends and neighbours often gave them a complimentary day's ploughing, saving them considerable work. As an example, fifteen ploughs turned up to give a day's ploughing to James L. Shankland on taking over the tenancy of Garclaugh farm in New Cumnock in March 1902.

Ayrshire Farmers

Much of Ayrshire is associated with two industries – coalmining and agriculture. Unfortunately, coal-mining is no longer a large employer like it once was, today only open cast coal mines existing. A similar story can be told of farming – today agriculture does not employ anywhere near as many people as it once did. Much of this is down to the introduction of more and more machinery to lighten the load of the farmer, from tractors that work the fields to simpler things like milking machinery, reducing the requirements for as many dairymen and women.

Land was held by significant landowners across the county – the Marquis of Ailsa, earls of Eglinton, Dumfries, Loudoun, Glencairn, Dundonald, and a host of lower ranks owned the bulk of the county. There were fewer 'bonnet lairds' owning their own property – most farmers were tenants on estates and held leases of around nine or nineteen years. This resulted in many families moving from farm to farm as their leases expired – usually trying to better themselves by taking on larger holdings. Some families remained at the same farm, even for centuries, like the Howies who tenanted Lochgoin, Fenwick parish, or the Hoods of Hoodston in the parish of Stair.

The price of land has increased over the centuries – in 1760 good agricultural land could be leased for between five shillings to ten shillings per acre. Tenant farmers could earn up to £100 per annum from selling stock and produce. At the same time ploughmen earned £8 each year; poorer ploughmen got £5. Dairymaids earned £3 and shepherds got £1 16s.

In the 1770s agriculture underwent a major revolution in the county, as it did across the country, with many new innovations, like fences or hedges, being introduced. At the same time many small holdings were merged to form larger farms, and the number of labourers required reduced, resulting in the growth of villages. The larger estates developed their property, building new roads and farmhouses, planting trees and introducing draining.

The photograph shows the four Wardrop brothers, family and friends, at work at Garlaff farm, near Cumnock, probably in the early 1880s. They later became tenants then owners on various other farms in the Cumnock and Auchinleck areas.

ASD-598

Ploughing Matches

The first tractors appeared on Ayrshire farms in the 1940s, replacing the horses and Clydesdales that had been used for centuries to carry out the work. A tractor could do the job of many horses, and soon horsemen were either retrained as tractormen or made redundant.

Ploughing matches have been held in Ayrshire for many years. Originally, the matches were for horse-drawn ploughs, but with the arrival of the tractor these developed into tractor-drawn ploughing competitions.

Most parishes had their own competition, and in many cases the Highland Society offered a medal to the best ploughman. Prizes varied from the best at ploughing in senior and junior level, as well as 'extras over the field' which were more fun prizes. At Cumnock District Ploughing Society's match at Knockroon farm in January 1913, these included 'Best outs and ins', 'Tidiest turnout, nothing borrowed', 'Quietest working horses' and 'Best looking bachelor'.

A number of clubs were formed to run the competitions, such as Mauchline Tractor Ploughing Association, founded in 1944 by some local farmers who had become mechanised.

This photograph is of a tractor at a ploughing match held in a field at a farm near New Cumnock. The tractor is a Fordson N and it is drawing a twin-bladed plough. This is a trailing-type of plough, fixed to the tractor drawbar, hence the need for the wheels. A trip was activated to raise or lower it. This plough is actually a redeveloped implement that would have been pulled by a horse, as many early tractor implements were.

Ploughing was often carried out in November, when corn was planted on stubble fields. Fields for grass were usually ploughed in February, though often grass was also planted at the same time as corn, the grass growing later when the corn was harvested.

There were two Begg companies in Ayrshire that made ploughs and other implements, one based in Tarbolton and another based in Dalry. Robert Begg & Son Ltd of Dalry still existed in the late 1950s, and made power-lift two-furrow tractor ploughs, self-lift single-furrow digger tractor ploughs, and a variety of horse implements including swing ploughs, grubbers, harrows and other machinery.

MASSEY-FERGUSON
TCS
50

Ploughing Competition

The contestants in the photograph are unknown, but it is thought that the picture, probably taken sometime in the early 1960s, was taken at Parkhill farm, in the parish of Tarbolton. The tractor is a Massey Ferguson 35, beloved of many farmers, and it is drawing a Begg double-furrow plough.

Tilling of soil is as ancient as history itself, and over the years developments have been made in ploughs, used to turn over the soil. John Finlayson invented a number of agricultural implements, including 'Finlayson's Rid Plough'. This was based on Small's Plough, but was made from iron with a crane necked beam rising from the point where the coulter enters it, so as to form an easy curve with the top of the coulter. According to John Claudius Loudon's *Encyclopaedia of Agriculture*, published in 1825, 'it is an implement which may be of use under particular circumstances, but by no means generally.'

In the *Gentleman's Magazine* of July 1821 (Vol. 130), there is a report on Finlayson's new plough being tried out:

New Invented Plough. On Thursday, the 6th of September, Mr. John Finlayson, from Muirkirk, exhibited his new-invented plough in the parish of Lesmahagow, before a great number of the heritors, farmers, and ploughmen, of the parish and neighbourhood. Mr. Finlayson went to work on very rough benty land, which he ploughed with great speed and much ease, sometimes with one, and at other times by two horses, always making excellent work, and never having his plough so much as once choked up during the day. Although the plough in question be peculiarly well fitted for either paring or ploughing moss or benty land, and will do more work in one day than could possibly be done by ten men; yet there is no description of ground which it is not fitted to dress in a very superior manner by a change of its irons, which can be done in half a minute. It was tried by several experienced ploughmen, who all declared that, they never held any plough that was more easily managed or directed.

Harrowing with Horses

After the fields have been ploughed the clods of earth forming the furrows are broken down by harrowing in preparation for sowing. The seed was then sown on the broken soil and the ground was usually harrowed once more, covering the seed to protect it from the birds.

Harrows are basically frames with spikes projecting from them, the spikes passing through the soil of the furrows and breaking them down (or raking them) into smaller chunks. The earliest reference to harrows in Scotland dates from 1375 and they were often pulled by oxen in the older days, latterly by horses and more recently by tractor. In some more primitive agricultural areas, smaller harrows were pulled by tying them to horses' tails, but this was latterly seen as being cruel.

Horse-drawn harrows as shown in the picture were dragged by chains affixed to the horse's yoke. In harder soils, the harrows were sometimes drawn by pairs of horses, or horse and ox. The horse drew the harrows along the furrows, guided from the back by the farmer.

Harrows were usually made from wooden battens which were joined together to form a grid pattern. From the crossings long iron spikes projected downwards, sometimes as large as eight or ten inches, especially on 'break-harrows', which were used to break up the fallows after ploughing.

This photograph was taken at Greenock Mains farm, west of Muirkirk, perhaps around March. The farmer is Malcolm Jardine, and he is working a Clydesdale horse. He is probably preparing the field for oats, barley being more common as a crop from the 1960s.

In the old kirkyard at Muirkirk is an obelisk commemorating John Finlayson (1778-1826), inventor of Finlayson's plough and harrow. He also wrote a book entitled *Practical Instructions to Ploughmen: On the art of ploughing; with a dissertation on the powers and properties of the plough*, published by Constable in 1823. Finlayson's 'Scotch harrow' was to be made in vast quantities by Ransome, one of the largest implement makers in Britain. It was noted for its self-cleaning abilities.

Rolling the Fields

Taken in early spring, perhaps around April, in 1948, this picture shows the farmer rolling the fields with a roller prior to growing hay. The picture was taken near to New Cumnock, the farmer directing the Clydesdale horse with a set of reins.

Fields which previously had cattle or sheep in them tend to be turned up in places, the cattle hooves making holes in the ground, and areas around gates becoming churned up. Also, over time, stones tend to make their way to the surface, and rolling flattens all of these lumps down, so that the hay-cutting machinery will have less chance of being damaged. Rolling still takes place on farms where grass is grown for silage.

Clydesdales were the horse of choice for farm work, their strength and reliability being used by the farmer. Historically, farms may have had one or two horses on them. In 1798 a Farm Horse Tax was applied in Scotland, and details of how many horses there were on each farm being noted in the returns.

Clydesdales were bred in the county, the better stallions being taken around the district to service the mares. Some owners specialised in the hiring of their stallions, and in some cases syndicates were formed, like the North Ayrshire Horse Breeding Syndicate. Advertising cards were issued, such as the one which noted:

> Season 1916. The choicely-bred Clydesdale stallion 'The Cuff Lad' (18,943), the property of Dougald MacNeil, Cuff Farm, Beith, will serve mares in this district. Terms: £1 payable at end of season and £2 additional payable in May 1917, unless the Mare has not proved in Foal.

Probably the most famous Clydesdale in Ayrshire was the 'Baron of Buchlyvie', a horse that resulted in a major court case which eventually ended up at the House of Lords. Ownership of the twelve-year-old horse was disputed, and it was decided that it should be put on sale at Ayr market in 1911. The first bid of £3,000 matched the world record for a Clydesdale stallion, but bidding continued, and eventually it was sold for £9,500. The anonymous bidder turned out to be one of the owners, William Dunlop of Dunure Mains.

Sowing Seed with Sowing Sheet

A couple of pages back shows a photograph of the fields being harrowed after ploughing. The field may have already been sown with seed. Once the soil is broken down and levelled, the farmer used to walk across the field scattering the seed by hand.

A sowing sheet, or 'sawing sheet' is hung around the neck, and this was filled with seed. The sheet was made with a D-shaped timber frame, the thin pieces of wood being bent to form the shape. Over this a canvas bag was fixed, and a rope or strap was attached to it, to allow the sheet to be suspended from the neck.

The farmer walked along the lines of the furrows, scattering the seed onto the ground, forming an arc in front of him. The soil could then be rolled with a heavy stone or iron roller to compact it once more.

The sowing sheets were heavy, when loaded with seed or fertiliser, and the method of scattering required the sower to walk in a methodical way, one step forward at the same time as the hand was sowing. If the sower ended up out of step then his knees would buckle and he could land on the ground!

In the eighteenth century the seed was carried with a linen sheet, which was tied round the left shoulder and which carried around half a bushel. In many cases, fertiliser was also spread using this method. A typical older fertiliser was Nitro Chalk. This was delivered to railway goods stations, where the farmer had to travel to collect it.

Sowing was later mechanised, and various implements drawn behind horses were created to make the spreading of seed or manure much simpler. Jack & Sons of Maybole patented a 'manure distributor' which was horse-drawn. It had a container for the manure seed, which dropped down onto spinning discs, powered by gears from the cartwheels. Seed drills were also produced, originally drawn by horse but latterly converted and powered by tractors.

The farmer sowing the seed in this picture is Matt Halbert, the farm being Greenock Mains, located between Muirkirk and Sorn.

Shepherd and his Lamb

Shepherds have to tend their flock of sheep all year round, often requiring a long walk across the hills to check on them. Shepherds have their own trusty sheepdogs, which know every whistle and command that he makes, and they know instinctively what the shepherd is aiming to do with the sheep. The dogs here are Border collies, of the bare-skinned variety. These are often preferred by some shepherds as they are easier to keep clean.

This photograph shows William Dickson, who was the shepherd at Lambdoughty, near Straiton, in the 1940s. He tended the sheep on the hills on the farm for around forty years. He died around 1950 at the age of 84. He is carrying a young Blackface lamb – the picture was probably taken around April, when the lambing season was at its height. Over a short period of weeks, lambing is an intensive part of the shepherd's calendar, for he has to be available at any hour to check up on the ewes in case of difficulties.

Around the 'herd's neck he is carrying a lambing bag, basically a strap supporting a hessian bag, containing the important items needed for lambing on the hill. This could include iodine and string for helping at the birth, and a bottle with a rubber teet for feeding some lambs whose mothers were unable to, or else had rejected them for whatever reason.

To identify the sheep that belonged to different owners, sheep marks were introduced. These were different marks of colour on the fleece that identified which farm the sheep belonged to. In 1923 nearly 260 farms in Carrick were issued with sheep marks.

Many old shepherds' cottages in the uplands of Ayrshire were located in remote places, especially in the south and eastern parts of the county. Some of the more remote cottages included Tunskeen and Ferter, both in Barr parish, which did not have any roadway or track leading to them. Shepherds staying at such houses had to carry all of their requirements to the house, often over a long distance. As time passed, shepherds were unwilling to live so remotely, and these cottages were abandoned, usually becoming ruinous.

Sheep Shearing

The hill country around Ayrshire is ideal for breeding sheep. Every summer, usually in June or July, these sheep are sheared for their wool, and shepherds often have to shear thousands at a time. The shepherd would keep his eye open for the 'rise', or new wool growing in the fleece, to reach the length of half an inch or more. The larger the rise the easier the sheep was to clip. The time taken to clip a sheep with hand shears varied, but could be from five to ten minutes, depending on the experience of the clipper.

When clipped, the wool was rolled, and then packed away in wool bags. The fleeces from Blackface sheep were rolled with the outside to the outside, whereas other breeds were rolled with the inside facing out. The large bags for fleeces were hung from the rafters of a shed, and around thirty fleeces fitted in them – young lads being put into the bags to trample the fleeces down. The bags were then sewn closed using string supplied by the Wool Marketing Board.

This old photograph shows John Sykes and his two sons at Old Smithston farm, near to Patna. John Sykes was the shepherd at Old Smithston for 38 years. Smithston farm was owned for many years by the MacIndoe family, before they emigrated to Australia to take up farming there. At one time Smithston farm extended to around 1,400 acres, climbing east from the River Doon to the heights above Rankinston and Patna, a distance of four miles from east to west. At its highest point, the farm reached 1407 feet above sea level at Kilmein Hill. At the time the farm had forty score of breeding ewes, numerous hill, or beef, cattle and sixty milking Ayrshire cattle.

One of the largest sheep farms in Ayrshire at one time was Starr, which sits at the top end of Loch Doon. Old accounts of this farm claim that it extended to 7,777 acres, and the countryside covered by it was so rough that it was only useful for breeding sheep.

Dipping Sheep

Each July, or thereabouts, after the sheep have been clipped and their fleeces removed, they require to be dipped in a bath of insecticide and fungicide chemicals. These are used to treat a number of serious external parasites which included scab, blow fly and ticks. Originally, the dip was an organo-phosphorus type, a rather toxic chemical which was harmful to the skin and local watercourses, should it reach them. Other forms included Cypermethrin. This type of dip is now banned.

On sheep farms, various types of bucht or fold were constructed for working with the stock. Traditionally, circular stone dikes were constructed, sometimes with projecting walls at an angle, to assist helping in getting the sheep into them. On larger farms, more extensive folds were built, sometimes of stone if there was a plentiful and ready supply of it, though many were to be built of timber and corrugated iron, as seen in this picture.

The sheep are brought from the fields to the folds, or pens, and directed to a narrow passageway in which the tank is located. The sheep is forced through the water, often having to be pushed in, though the mass of sheep behind it helps to push them along. When the sheep lands in the dip, the farmer or shepherd often pushes it further into the liquid by using a stick on which is a shaped head which is placed on the back of the sheep.

Once the sheep have been plunged into the chemical, a ramp allows the ewe to climb back out of the pool, and they are kept in a pen for a time to allow the chemical to run off.

Today, sheep dipping is often carried out by a contractor, a mobile dipping unit being brought to the farm steading and the sheep passed through it. The world's first sheep dip was invented by George Wilson of Coldstream in 1830. The liquid dip was based on arsenic powder.

This photograph was taken in 1994 at Waistland farm, in the parish of New Cumnock, owned by the Young family, the boy watching being Graham Young. Today, health and safety rules would prevent such observing.

Dressing Tups for the Market

Tups, or rams, were highly prized assets on hill farms, and they could achieve high figures in sales at certain markets if they were of good quality. This old photograph, probably taken somewhere on the Craigengillan estate, in the Dalmellington area, shows three shepherds in the process of dressing tups prior to them being taken to the market. The most likely destination was the Newton Stewart tup sale, which is still one of the most important in Scotland. Ram sales are usually held in October.

The tups have large horns which grow from their head in a curly fashion, and which are prized by shepherds and others for making crooks and walking sticks. Tup horns have more solid material than ewe horns, and can be carved into ornate handles, something that the shepherd would pass his time with in the long winter nights.

One of the more famous breeders of Blackface tups in Ayrshire was Charles Howatson of Glenbuck (1832-1918). He was a major landowner in the east of the county at one time, his estate covering considerable areas across Auchinleck, Sorn and Muirkirk parishes. At Crossflatt, near Muirkirk, he bred Blackface sheep with the intention of making them survive the weather of the uplands. These developed a fleece that was so thick and which covered the sheep so fully that they could survive the severest weather. From 1864-88 the average weight of their fleeces increased from 3¼ pounds to 6½ pounds. In 1903 his 'Morning Sun' won the Highland Show, which was held in Dumfries that year. In fact, Howatson won the blue ribbon twelve years in succession for shearling rams. In 1909 he was presented with a silver salver, candelabra and other items from a collection of breeders of blackface sheep for his part in improving their stock.

Blackface sheep and rams are still bred widely across Ayrshire today. They are preferred because of their hardiness in surviving the weather, as well as for the quality wool produced, used primarily in the carpet and tweed industry. There are around 400,000 sheep on Ayrshire farms and probably around 10,000 tups.

Ayrshire Cattle

The photograph shows Ayrshire cattle leaving the farm after being milked and returning to the field. The picture was taken around 1938-40. A nineteenth century verse describes Ayrshire cattle:

Would you know how to judge of a good Ayrshire cow?
Attend to the lesson you'll hear from me now;
Her head should be short, and her muzzle good size;
Her nose should be fine between muzzle and eyes;
Her eyes full and lively; forehead ample and wide;
Horns wide, looking up, and curved inwards beside;
Her neck should be a fine tapering wedge,
And free from loose skin on the undermost edge;
Should be fine where 'tis joined with the seat of the brain;
Strong and straight appear line without hollow or mane;
Shoulder-blades should be thin where they meet at the top;
Let her brisket be light, nor resemble a crop;
Her fore-part recede like the lash of a whip,
And strongly resemble the bow of a ship;
Her back short and straight, with the spine well defined,
Especially where back, neck, and shoulders are joined;
Her ribs short and arched, like the ribs of a barge;
Body deep at the flanks, and milk-veins full and large;
Pelvis long, broad, and straight, and in some measure flat;
Hock-bones wide apart and not bearing much fat;
Her thighs deep and broad, neither rounded nor flat;
Her tail long and fine and joined square with her back;
Milk-vessel capacious, and forward extending,
The hinder part broad and to body fast pending;
The sole of her udder should just form a plane,
And all the four teats equal thickness attain;
Their length not exceeding two inches or three;
They should hang to the earth perpendicularly;
Their distance apart, when they're viewed from behind,
Will include about half of the udder you'll find;
And when viewed from the side, they will have at each end
As much of the udder as 'tween them is penned;
Her legs should be short and bones fine and clean,
The points of the latter being quite firm and keen;
Skin soft and elastic as the cushions of air,
And covered all over with short woolly hair;
The colours preferred are confined to a few,
Either brown and white checkered or all brown will do;
The weight of the animal leaving the stall,
Should be about five hundred sinking offal.

Milking the Kye

The byre here is typical of hundreds of byres that exist across the county. Byres were usually formed as elongated buildings, the door at one end. Running up the centre is the 'gang' or walkway, in this byre marked in a cross-grid fashion to aid grip, both for the cattle and the dairyman, when the way is wet.

To either side is the 'grip', the channel where dung and urine is dropped, the liquid running down the length of the byre and out the door, the dung lying until the farmer, or usually a young farmhand, was given the job of cleaning it out with a 'graip' or shovel and a barrow. The dung was then transported to the midden.

The cubicles where the cattle were tethered, usually by a chain around their necks, were locally known as a 'biss'. These often held two cows, allowing the milking machine to be located between the two cows, which could be milked at the same time. At the head of each biss were feeding troughs and usually a water bowl, the water controlled by a valve operated by the cow itself – its nose pushing a flap or lever which released the water into the bowl.

Most byres of this type have been replaced by larger milking parlours, many of which are now self-operating, a robot placing the milking machine on the udders, and cattle walking into them when they feel that they are ready for milking.

The photograph was taken in the byre at Laigh Corton farm, near Ayr, in the 1960s. The people in the picture are Bill Tennant, John Hutton and Mary Hutton. Bill Tennant was a television presenter for STV who took part in news and current affairs programmes. Although he lived in a large house in Glasgow, he often spent much of his time living in a caravan at High Corton. He was noted for his 'couthy homilies'.

At the time of Robert Burns, Laigh Corton was tenanted by John Tennant, a friend of the poet as well as his father. It is thought that he was a witness at Burns' baptism. John Tennant was later to take on the lease of Glenconner, in Ochiltree parish, and from him descends the present Lord Glenconner. At the Tennant seat of Glen House, near Peebles, is an old horn that came from a cow belonging to Laigh Corton, but which escaped and ended up in Alloway kirk.

Milking in the Byre

Almost every farm in Ayrshire that had any improved grassland had a dairy. Adjoining the farm house was the byre, where the cows were brought in twice each day for milking. Originally milking was done by hand, the dairyman and any assistants he had would work their way along the byre, milking the cattle into pails. As things developed milking machines were introduced, self-contained units that drew the milk from the udder by using a vacuum line. The pipeline suspended from the rafters in this picture indicates that this system was in use in this byre.

A single milking can was placed between the two cows in the cubicle. There were two milking machines which were placed on the udders of the cow to either side, and a rubber pipe was affixed to the overhead vacuum line. The sucking milked both cows at the same time. When the milking was completed, the milk from the can was poured into the cooler, usually located in an adjoining building called the dairy.

Progress continued, and the milk was passed along stainless steel pipes to a large tank, usually located in another room. This was kept at a cool temperature. This milk was then pumped into the tanker which called at the farm daily, collecting milk and transporting it to larger creameries or bottling plants.

Milk was for many years the main product of Ayrshire farms, the county producing around one quarter of the total milk consumed in Scotland. In 1946, 31 million gallons were produced, of which 70% was sent outwith the county. Most of the production was sent to the Scottish Milk Marketing Board, but this was disbanded and different buyers now take most of the milk, selling it on to the supermarkets. To counteract the monopoly of the larger buyers, Sorn Milk was established in 1994, buying milk for local farms and selling it on to the creamery at Lockerbie in Dumfriesshire.

This picture shows William Howat in the byre at Mill Affleck, around 1950. He is carrying two milk pails, the fact that they were used for milk being obvious from their cleanliness. He has a herd of Ayrshire cattle.

Milk Deliveries

Across the county numerous farmers had their own dairy which produced milk that was taken regularly to the local towns for sale to the residents. This picture was taken in May 1935 at Bowton farm, which lies to the south-west of Cumnock. The farmer has four churns of milk (which would hold ten gallons each) on a small cart which he is taking to Skares Station. This would be the farm's daily production.

The supply of milk gradually became more mechanised, with the establishment of bottling plants at some farms. Sales of milk became quite competitive in some communities, for example in Mauchline in the 1950s there were at least three businesses – the High Street Dairy, with 'fresh supplies of T.T. milk daily', Mosshead Dairy Farm, where their 'milk [was] bottled on our own farm by modern methods', and James Hodge of Bogwood farm, regularly delivering each morning in Mauchline and Ochiltree. Their advertising strap line was 'Bogwood milk for bonnie babies.'

Production of milk in the county has varied over the years. In the 1940s over 48,000 cows were milked twice daily, in a few cases three times per day. In 1934 26,874,835 gallons of milk was produced. By 1946 this had increased to 31,311,913 gallons. In 1951 new regulations were introduced, classifying milk into two grades – Tuberculin Tested and Pasteurised. Around the same time foil tops were introduced, protecting the pouring lip of the bottle. A good return from an Ayrshire cow was in the region of 12,000 pounds of milk per annum, with about 4% butter fat.

Larger dairies were established supplying milk to wider areas. One of the more successful was Stevenson's Dairy Farms, based at Changue farm, near Cumnock. The firm was established in 1870, but gradually grew to have five or six farms, producing milk which was bottled at Changue. A fleet of milk lorries transported the milk across the central part of the county, in 1954 being 15 in number, delivering to 5,000 homes. Unable to compete with ever-increasing centralisation, the milk business was sold in 2003 to Graham's Dairies of Bridge of Allan.

THE DAIRY SCHOOL
FOR
SCOTLAND

The Dairy School for Scotland

In the 1880s there was a concern that the standard of agricultural produce in the district was falling. The Scottish Dairy Association decided to give lectures in the county, trying to educate the farmers on better ways to produce milk, cheese, butter and other foodstuffs. Soon, it was realised that a school would be a better way forward, and in 1889 a dairy at Holmes farm, near Kilmarnock, was taken over and a school started there. The milk was purchased from the farmer at Holmes, and the pupils were shown how to make cheese. They were later to have lessons in botany and chemistry.

In 1900 a new agricultural college was established, based in John Street, Ayr, with the Dairy School becoming part of it. Poultry classes were also introduced at Holmes. In the same year Holmes farm was leased in total, at a cost of £400 per annum.

It was soon discovered that the school was too small, so a new specially-constructed dairy school was erected, designed by Allan Stevenson of Ayr. This was opened on 11 June 1904 and is shown in the photograph. One of the principal proponents of the school was Joseph Harling Turner of Cessnock Castle, who was the honorary secretary.

By 1927 the college had outgrown its premises at Kilmarnock and it was decided to look for a larger site. There were 503 students at the time, a drop from 611 a few years earlier. Where to establish a new college was being debated when John M. Hannah of Girvan Mains offered them 913 acres of the estate of Auchincruive. This was formally accepted on 5 December 1927.

Within the grounds of Auchincruive House a new college was established, officially opened in June 1931. On the opposite side of the road from Auchincruive a new institute of dairying was built, named the Hannah Dairy Research Institute in honour of the benefactor. The building was designed by A. G. Ingham and opened in 1931. The Dairy School at Kilmarnock was closed when the new building was erected at Auchincruive.

Hide & Skin Dealers

Everything that could be used from cattle and sheep on farms was used in the past on a more local scale. This old photograph shows a horse and cart belonging to the 'Ayrshire Hide and Skin' dealing company, probably sometime after the First World War. The cart is loaded with fleece-covered skins from sheep which were being taken from the slaughterhouse to the tannery.

In charge of the cart and horse is William Ralston Woodside (1871-1929), who lived in Kilwinning, and who was also a butcher. He spent most of his life working as a drover, and often took cattle or sheep along the byways of Ayrshire, from farms to the markets. He hauled hides from the slaughter houses to the tan works in Irvine. At one time the tannery was located at the Seagatefoot, but it was taken over in 1812 by the burgh and converted into the slaughter house.

Most small towns in Ayrshire had their own tanneries, where hides were cured and could then be used for making shoes and other leather items. Places like Maybole were celebrated for the number and size of tanneries, the town being famous for its leather works. Businesses such as Gray's produced shoes, and at one time 12,360 pairs of shoes were manufactured in Maybole each week.

Smaller tanneries existed in other communities, such as that in Girvan, located between Bridge Street and the Water of Girvan. A large boiler was used for cleaning the hides, and in the yard were 21 large tanks for soaking the hides. In the mid nineteenth century the tannery was run by David Law and John MacIlwraith. The tannery in Cumnock survives in name only – Tanyard being one of the main routes through the town.

In Ayr the tanning of leather was a major business, with tanneries located in Mill Street. In 1790 around 3,000 hides were tanned and from 500 to 600 dozens of calf skins. The old tannery in Saltcoats had 'handlers and spenders ... lime-pits and water-holes, steam engine and bark mill, lime stores, drying sheds, currying shops and offices.'

Wm WATT, FENWICK
Phone. 29 Fenwick.
WILLIAM WATT, HAULAGE CONTRACT
VS-2617

Fertiliser Deliveries

Manure was sold around the farms for scattering on the fields to promote growth. The round white grains contain a chemical that encourages the grass to grow, increasing the yield at harvest time, when it was cut, dried and stored for use as fodder during the winter months. These pellets are known as 'prills', being made by spraying droplets of molten fertiliser into the top of a tall tower.

This picture shows William Hamilton Watt (1890-1969) who sold manure and other items around the Kilmarnock area. He lived in Fenwick and with his brother Johnny Watt he was able to set up in business in the 1920s, travelling around the farms with feeding and fertiliser. The partnership was later split, and William continued to work on his own. At the outbreak of the Second World War the lorry was taken away from him for use in the war effort and he went to work as a driver for James Campbell, grain merchants in Kilmarnock, as they had bought a lorry to make deliveries. Companies were allowed to have lorries to supply goods to farmers during the Second World War. The lorry shown is an Albion, which was made in a factory in Glasgow.

Fertiliser was manufactured on a small scale in Ayrshire, in the late eighteenth century barilla, black ash and soda being created for agricultural purposes. In 1838 Taylor's Newton saltworks commenced the manufacture of bonemeal fertiliser by crushing bones taken from the slaughterhouses.

In 1860 A. Weir & Co. set up a factory in Ayr for the production of superphosphate, the first such factory in the west of Scotland. This business was taken over by Daniel Wyllie and Co. in 1880. In 1926 this firm merged into Scottish Agricultural Industries (becoming part of ICI in 1928), and by the end of the Second World War employed around 200 workers. In 1947 the factory was substantially rebuilt, a large fertiliser works constructed at the site on the Newton Shore, for the manufacture of grain fertiliser. This was further expanded in 1961. Part of the works was designed by Sir Basil Spence, more noted as the architect responsible for the modern Coventry Cathedral.

Tummlin' Tam

The tummlin' tam, or hay-sweep, was first used in Scotland in the early nineteenth century. The cut grass, once it had dried in the sun, was gathered together using the hay-rake, then collected into larger piles by the tummlin' tam, which was drawn behind a horse. Chains were connected to either end of the main timber shaft. The operator guided the tummlin' tam along the windrows of cut hay using the two handles at the back, the long spikes pushing across the ground a few inches above the soil and gathering up the lengths of hay. Once the required amount of hay had been gathered in the spikes, and the desired location had been reached, the operator tilted the spikes slightly, so that they caught in the ground. The pulling horse continued, causing the tummlin' tam to tip over, or somersault, hence the name, releasing the pile of hay. The tummlin' tam righted itself again, and the operator had to either run round the pile of hay or jump over it to catch the implement and start again.

The gathered piles of hay were then assembled into hay-ricks, seen in the background of the picture. These ricks could then be lifted complete by special rick lifters. These comprised of single-axled bogeys, which could be tipped down at the back and pushed up to the base of the rick. A rope or two was fed round the rick, and these were attached to a pulley mounted at the front end of the bogey. The ropes were then hauled by the pulley, resulting in the rick being dragged up onto the rick-lifter. Once the rick reached the middle of the axles, the equilibrium caused the bogey to tip up to the horizontal position, and the weight was taken by the horse. The ricks could then be drawn back to the farm steading for rebuilding as haystacks.

This photograph shows a break for lunch during the lifting of the hay by the tummlin' tam at Barglachan farm, near Auchinleck. It dates from around 1954 and shows the farmer, Thomas Templeton, and a group of helpers. In the background can be seen a water tank, constructed by Ayr County Council in 1912 as part of the Loch Bradan water scheme.

Hay Rake

When the grass that had been cut for hay and left to dry for a few days in the field was ready, it was collected into long lines known as windrows. To do this, hay-rakes were used. These were iron implements which were drawn behind horses. The ones in the photographs have iron wheels, affixed onto a frame. The operator sat on a metal seat in the middle of the hay rake, and led the horse across the fields. Behind, the tines of the hay rake dragged on the ground, gathering up the loose pieces of hay in the space before them. At intervals, the operator could operate a leaver that lifted the tines free of the ground, releasing the pile of hay.

Normally, the operator would lower the rake for around twenty yards or so, depending on how thick the hay was, then lift the rake using the lever, and keep repeating this until the machine had criss-crossed the whole field and all the hay had been dragged into windrows.

Many of the Ayrshire agricultural implement manufacturers produced hay rakes, including Alexander Jack of Maybole. The ones shown here were dump rakes, wide two-wheeled implements with curved steel or iron teeth or tines, usually operated from a seat mounted over the rake with a lever-operated lifting mechanism.

The woman operating the hay rake in the left-hand picture was Margaret Collins, working at Barglachan farm, Auchinleck, probably around 1954. The other picture shows a hay-rake in use at Laight farm, in Glen Afton, south of New Cumnock. George Houston is the lad on top of the haystack.

On larger farms, rick-lifting cranes were used to lift complete ricks from rick-lifters up onto the stack. These comprised large 'A'-frames with a swinging derrick. Ropes were tied onto poles that were placed under the ricks, and by using a Clydesdale horse, the main rope was pulled, hauling up the rick.

Baling Hay

In June or July, and sometimes August, depending on the summer weather, hay was traditionally harvested for winter feed for cattle. Grass was grown in fields and this was cut, left to dry for a time, then roaded up and baled into square bales, as shown in this photograph of 1965. The bales were transported back to the steading, where they were kept in haysheds and used over the winter months.

Developments in baling have taken place over the years, the old square bales shown here being replaced in most cases by large round bales, which were left in the fields and then carried back to the farm and stored in piles. These bales could often be lifted whole and unrolled within the shed, meaning that the process of feeding cattle was more mechanised than in the past.

Following a particularly bad summer, most farmers in Ayrshire moved from hay to silage. This allowed the grass to be cut and harvested within the same day, the grass lifted by a chopper, which in most cases was hired from a contractor, and blown into a silage trailer. The grass was carried back to the farm, where silage pits were used to store it, the grass rolled to remove as much air as possible, and polythene covered with old car tyres placed over the top.

This photograph was taken on Dumfries House Estate, near Cumnock, in a field known as the Symington Field. The origin of this name is no longer known, but on many farms across Ayrshire the fields have traditional names. Many of these are being forgotten, or else how they got their name is, a great loss to local history. Other fields on Dumfries estate had names like Temple Park, Brick Park, Balance Holm, Damelonians, West and East Snaids, and Wilderness.

The two men in the picture are John Kirkland (left) and Ronald Graham. The latter was to be one of agriculture's accidental death statistics, for in 1974 he was killed when his coat caught in a power take off shaft connected to a slurry tanker.

Building Haystacks

The gathering of hay to store for winter feeding occurred on almost every farm across the county. Grass was grown to be cut for hay in the summer. The grass was left to dry in the fields for a few days before being gathered into windrows, or lines of hay. The windrow usually collected the hay from five ridges. These rows were then piled in small ricks to dry further before being collected by horse and cart, or tractor and trailer in more recent times. The bundles were carted back to the farm and piled up in round haystacks.

The building of haystacks was something of an art form, and usually the head of the farm made sure that they were built to a high standard, as neighbouring farmers would be looking over the dikes to see how each farm had prepared for the winter. The ground next to the farm where the stacks were built is known as the stackyard. Haystacks were built on raised bases, sometimes on an elevated foundation, comprising round pillars, often made from stone, but in the nineteenth century some manufacturers sold cast iron pillars. Across the top of the pillars wooded battens could be placed, forming a base on which the stack could be built. The raising of the haystack off the ground prevented dampness from rising from the bottom, as well as stopping mice or rats from climbing into the stack and building nests.

Once the stack was built the top layer had a primitive form of thatch over it, shedding the rainwater from the top. To stop the hay from blowing away, ropes were tied over the top, forming a pattern, sometimes diamond-shaped, in other cases radiating from the top. At other times nets were used to cover the stacks.

The builder of the stacks in the picture to the left was Hugh Brown Howat, constructing them in the stackyard at Mill Affleck, between Auchinleck and Ochiltree. The corn stacks in the right-hand picture are located at Barmickhill farm, Cumnock.

GHS 245

Bringing in the Ricks

The photograph shows Robert Kerr bringing in a rick at Linnhead farm, Dunlop parish, using a Ferguson T20 tractor. The picture was taken around 1950 soon after tractors became readily available and more affordable on Ayrshire farms. In 1930 there were only 92 tractors in the county; by 1946 the number grew to 1,135, almost one per average-sized farm.

Hay ricks were formed in the fields and were dotted across the hay meadows. Older rick lifters were pulled by horses, and basically comprised a form of trailer, which could be tipped over, so that one end lay on the ground. Ropes and pulleys were then used to draw the rick onto the trailer, and when it reached the half-way point, the centre of gravity was such that it tipped the trailer back into the upright position, allowing the horse to draw it back to the yard.

Alexander Jack of Maybole was noted for its horse-drawn hayrick lifters. An article in the Glasgow Weekly Herald of 1901 noted 'One specialty of the firm should have to be noted. It is called a hay-rick lifter, and transfers bodily the hay-rick from the field at a single effort. Constructed like a bevelled lorry, the bottom of the lifter rests on the ground, the ropes are put round the rick, and a handle at each side pulls the ropes tighter and tighter, dragging the rick on to the floor of the lifter, which is backed slowly under it. Contrasted with the old hay fork, this lifter is a great advance.'

The rick here is being carried back to the farm using a Dickie Campbell rick lifter. This was affixed to the implement three-point linkage on the back of the tractor. It looked similar to the later buck-rake, which was used to lift square bales, but it had more prongs instead.

The weight of the rick was such that the front end of the tractor often lifted off the ground. To prevent this, weights or heavy boulders lifted from the fields were placed in the box at the front of the engine. Weights were often bolted through the front wheels of the tractor also, helping to keep them on the ground.

Silage

The harvesting of grass to store for winter feed is something that has taken place on farms longer than history records. This has usually taken the form of hay, but in recent years silage has become the norm in most of the county. Developments in harvesting grass for hay have taken place for centuries, from the invention of rick-lifters to the introduction of balers. Older balers gathered the grass and compressed it into cuboid blocks, tied together with binder twine. Larger balers were introduced that created round bales, and these were the most up to date used in the shire.

However, in 1983, the summer weather was particularly bad, with long spells of rain. Many farms struggled to harvest their hay crop, especially in the higher parishes, and time passed with little let up in the weather. In many cases the hay had been cut but was unable to dry as it lay in the fields, the grass beginning to grow up between it.

In desperation, many farmers turned to silage for the first time. Silage pits were hastily dug into the ground, and the grass was harvested by choppers, hired in for the purpose. The grass was stored throughout the autumn under large polythene sheets, usually held down by used car tyres. The success of the silage that winter resulted in many farmers building proper silage pits the following year, and the baler was discarded to history.

The cost of choppers was such that most smaller farmers could not afford one, especially for such a short period in the year of the farm, so agricultural contractors set up, travelling from farm to farm through the summer months, harvesting the grass for the farmer. In most cases two cuts are taken, but in some areas three cuts of silage can be collected.

The photograph shows a Claas chopper lifting the grass for silage at Gallowhill farm, Coylton, in the early 1980s. John Hutton is driving, and the farm was occupied at that time by Eric Smith. Much of the land of Gallowhill has been built on by an expanding community at Coylton, seen in the background.

Drill Plough for Potatoes

When planting potatoes a drill plough was often used. This was usually used twice on the ground, the first draw across the ground being relatively shallow, forming low drills. The seed potatoes could then be planted by hand, a long and laborious task. Most of the seed potatoes planted across Ayrshire were bought from the north-east of Scotland. Once the potatoes were in the soil the drill plough was worked over the same ground, in the same direction, only on this occasion the blades were set lower, so that the soil was piled up in deeper drills, covering the potatoes. Older drill ploughs were horse-drawn, many of them being manufactured by local smiths.

This picture shows Jimmy Kirkland ploughing the Big Holm on Dumfries House Estate (with the mansion in the distance), west of Cumnock. The plough has three blades, and this plough is mounted on the back of a Fordson E27N tractor, which was powered with a petrol-paraffin mix. The photograph was taken around 1950, and at the time the potatoes were grown for the co-operative.

The growing of potatoes as a main crop on farms did not start in earnest until the 1700s. Once their potential was realised more and more acres were dedicated to the crop. To promote early potatoes, which earned a premium at market, the 'boxing' system was often used. This was a method whereby seed potatoes were stored in shallow boxes and encouraged to sprout prior to planting.

Around the time of the photograph, there were approximately 66,000 tons of potatoes produced in the county. This was in excess of six per cent of the Scottish output. Planting usually took place in February or March, the fields being heavily manured beforehand. In many cases, especially along the shore, the fields were watered to encourage growth, and the 'tatties' were lifted from the second week of June through to July. A later crop of 'earlies' was also farmed; this being lifted in August, and the main crop of potatoes were lifted in October.

FCS 96

Tattie Howking

The photograph was taken at Rigghead farm, near New Cumnock, on a day when the farmer was lifting the tatties from the ground using a tattie-lifter, drawn by a Ferguson T20 tractor. This machine ran along the rigs and threw the tatties to the side, hitting them off of a baffle which was designed to keep them in a line. Boys often took days off from the school at this time of year to work at various farms, and many old school log books, which were meticulously kept by the headmasters, often noted that attendance that day was low due to the numbers of pupils away lifting potatoes.

Potatoes were usually lifted in October or November. In some cases drill ploughs were used, these opening up the drills and allowing the lifter access. Spinner diggers were then developed, and in time elevator lifters were introduced (late 1920s), reducing the need for as many tattie-howkers.

A survey in 1856 found that 8,688 acres of potatoes had been planted in Ayrshire. This figure increased to a maximum of 11,434 acres in 1918, but it dropped once more, for in 1925 a survey of the county identified the nine main parishes that produced potatoes, totalling 5,923 acres. These were, in order of size, large to small, Girvan, Kirkoswald, West Kilbride, Ayr, Maybole, Dundonald, Monkton & Prestwick, Dailly and Ardrossan. Workers were often housed in small bothies, the conditions being far from ideal. On 21 September 1924 a fire broke out at Kilnford farm, Dundonald parish, resulting in nine tattie-howkers being suffocated by the smoke.

The development of the 'early' tattie was made in the Girvan area around 1860, at the same time as the arrival of the railway, which was used to transport the crop to the markets. It is reckoned that Quintin Dunlop of Morriston farm (near Kirkoswald) 'did more than almost anyone else to establish it commercially.' The Epicure variety of potato was found to be most suitable for early cropping, and this became the standard Ayrshire potato.

Potatoes were also grown for feeding pigs at one time, many of the tatties being kept for fattening pigs for the Ayrshire bacon industry.

Tattie Howking

Ayrshire tatties are famed across the country for being an early variety. Grown along the coast on the highly fertile soil, they are brought on under polythene during the early months of the year, so that the crop can be harvested and sold whilst the price of potatoes is high.

Historically, potatoes were grown more widely across the county, as this old photograph shows, dating from the Second World War. The potatoes are being harvested at Broomfield farm, the lands of which are now partially occupied by Visions Leisure Centre and Terringzean View houses in Cumnock. At the time this picture was taken, the only houses here are those of Auchinleck Road in the background, built at the foot of the old Stepends bing.

Potatoes were planted in drills opened up by the plough. Dung from the midden was spread along the bottom of the drills, the seed potato was placed on it, and the drill was closed over. In the 1930s the first mechanical potato planters were introduced, but these took time to catch on.

Harvesting potatoes was quite an intensive task, and thousands of labourers were employed when the potatoes were being lifted. Along the Carrick shore Irish workers were taken on for this task, being given accommodation in bothies on the farms.

Various methods were used to dig the potatoes prior to lifting them, drill-ploughs being drawn along the drills to lift the roots and spread them. Another machine developed to dig up the potatoes was a spinner digger, manufactured by Alexander Jack of Maybole. These were drawn behind horses or tractors and had large studded wheels which drove the digging blades. An older potato-digging machine was advertised by Pollock of Mauchline on 5 September 1877. This was 'the best machine for raising potatoes ever offered to the public. Perfect in work, light and easy to draw. A. Pollock has invented a much lighter machine, with broad-rimmed wrought iron wheels, admirably adapted for moss land or light soil.' In fact, it is a horse-drawn potato digger by Pollock that is shown in the picture.

Land Army at Dumfries House

During the Second World War, most young farmers were abroad, serving with the army, navy or air force. To compensate for the lack of labour, and to ensure the continuation of the supply of food in the country, what was termed the 'Land Girls' or Women's Land Army was formed on 1 June 1939. These were women who worked on farms, carrying out the jobs that would normally have been done by the men.

The women, many of whom came from the industrial cities of northern England, often had no experience of agricultural work. To compensate for this, short courses were organised to educate them, and Auchincruive College taught on average 400 members each year, reaching a maximum of 566 in 1941.

Women in the army earned 28 shillings a week, but had to use around half of it for board and lodgings. When a girl had worked for six months, and if she was living more than twenty miles from home, she would be allowed a free journey back, paid for by the Women's Land Army. They did not have a set holiday entitlement, paid or unpaid, it being left up to individual farmers to decide when a worker could take time off. The girls were issued with a uniform of brown dungarees, a matching jacket and wellington boots for work clothes, as well as a different set of clothes for when not working.

The Women's Land Army took over various properties in Ayrshire for the duration of the war. Trochrague House, near Girvan, was occupied by them. In June 1948 it was recorded that there were 302 members of the Women's Land Army still working on Ayrshire farms. The army was disbanded nationally in 1950.

The photograph shows some land girls at Dumfries House Home Farm, where they worked for the duration of the war. They are accompanied by two soldiers, perhaps prisoners of war from the nearby Pennylands camp, which was established on the estate. It is known that at least one of the land girls settled locally and married.

McCONNEL

Land Drainage

A group of farmers gather round a draining machine which was being demonstrated by William Pollock of Uplands, Coylton, at Darnlaw farm, Auchinleck, in the 1950s. Drainage has always been a problem in Ayrshire, the high precipitation in the west coast of Scotland meaning that fields tend to be much wetter than in other parts of the country. To assist in taking the excess water away, drying out the soil, and allowing the fields to be worked earlier, farmers have drained their fields for centuries.

The oldest draining methods used in Scotland were open ditches, drawing the water away. In time, these were replaced by rubble drains, lines of loose boulders and stone which allowed the water to percolate through the soil. However, as time passes these drains silted up.

In the late eighteenth century the use of clay drainage tiles was introduced, and this became the most popular method of draining fields in Ayrshire for many years. Tileworks were established all over the county to manufacture the tiles, which varied in section from U-shaped, rectangular shaped, to the more popular oval shape. The tiles were placed in open drains and then covered over.

Tileworks used local clay for the manufacture of the tiles. The clay was dug from the ground; sometimes it was mixed to improve its constituency, and then extruded through dies to make the required shape. The clay tile was then transported into the kiln and piled up, awaiting firing. Once the kiln had cooled down, it was emptied, and the tiles sold to farmers for use in draining. Dozens of these works existed all over Ayrshire, from Girvan in the south, to Kilbirnie in the north. One of the longest-lasting works was that at Ochiltree. In the background of the picture on page 2 one can see a pile of these clay tiles awaiting being laid.

The photograph shows trials of the new coiled plastic drain, laid in a furrow cut by the machine, which was hauled along by a large tractor. The coil was left in the ground and the weight of the machine closed the furrow behind it, preventing the need for a digger to excavate a channel.

Harvesting Ryegrass Seed

This pleasant scene shows the women working the fields at Clydenoch farm, in the parish of Ochiltree. They are collecting the blades of ryegrass, which was harvested for its seed. They are gathering it together and tying them into sheaves. In the fields ryegrass had to be carefully handled, for if the worker was too rough with it the heads fell onto the ground. Thus, they were carefully placed in sheaves, then stooks (usually six sheaves per stook), followed by 'huts' which had around thirty sheaves in them.

In the middle distance the men are working a horse-drawn reaper, pulled by a couple of horses. One of the main difficulties of harvesting ryegrass was that it was labour-intensive, and farmers often had difficulties in getting enough workers to do this. Once the grass was cut it had to be tied by hand, stooked and rickled a week later.

Ryegrass was grown for its good grass seed, and Ayrshire was the principal source of the seed, which was exported all over Great Britain. It was grown across the central belt of the county, on land that had medium to heavy soils. At one time the high prices paid for the seed made it a worthwhile crop. The seed was to be used the following year on newly-ploughed fields.

When the ryegrass was harvested, the stalks were historically threshed using a flail, two sticks joined together by knotted rope or leather thong, allowing them to be swivelled. Flails were usually held in the right hand, the handle around five feet long, the souple, or moving part, being between two and a half feet and three feet in length. Often the two parts were made from different types of wood – ash for the handle and hazel or blackthorn for the souple.

Ryegrass was also threshed in the threshing mill back at the farm, sometimes in half or two-thirds size mills. The difficulties in harvesting it meant that by the 1950s it was being abandoned as a crop.

Clydenoch farm was for many years part of the extensive Dumfries House Estate. It was long tenanted by the Sloans followed by the Wallaces. This photograph was taken in 1962.

M&S

Hay Seed Mill Day

At one time farms in the county grew their own crop of grass seed for use the following year in reseeding fields. One of the most popular crops was ryegrass, and Ayrshire was one of the biggest growers of this seed. The fields of ryegrass were cut when the grass had ripened and the seeds had fully formed, usually in August.

When cut, the grass was stooked the same as corn, and left for around three weeks to allow the seed to dry. Care had to be taken when gathering in ryegrass, as the seed was only held lightly in the husk and too much movement would knock it off in the fields, defeating the purpose of collecting it.

The ryegrass stooks were brought into the farm where it was threshed, to separate the seed from the rest of the stalk. Originally, this was done by hand on a threshing floor, but in time the process was mechanised. The seed being threshed here was most probably ryegrass, the large bags indicative of this to some extent, as ryegrass seed was comparatively light. The remaining stalks of the hay were kept and used for feeding purposes.

Much of the ryegrass was taken by Ayr seed merchants, MacGill & Smith, indicated by the M&S marking on the bags. This firm were major dealers in seed in Ayrshire, later becoming Sinclair MacGill. The firm was later taken over by Group Limagrain, the largest plant breeder and seed development company in Europe, but the Sinclair McGill name remains.

The farmer in the picture was Thomas Robertson, who is working at Broadwood farm, Stair, sometime around 1935-40. The growing of ryegrass for seed died out in the county around the early 1950s, after that time it being cheaper and less labour-intensive to buy in seed from elsewhere.

There have been a number of other long-established seed companies in the county. One of the oldest was William Samson in Kilmarnock, Burns' friend Tam Samson being a member of the family.

Threshing Machine

The threshing machine was used to remove the outer husks from grains of wheat. Before its invention the wheat had to be beaten with flails to separate the grains from the chaff, and then the grain had to be thrown into the air, or winnowed, to blow the chaff away. The man credited with creating the first successful threshing machine was Andrew Meikle (1719-1811), who lived in East Lothian. He had a few attempts at making a machine capable of this work, and his eventual design was patented in 1788. This is credited as being one of the most significant events in the agricultural revolution.

The threshing machine was often driven by a horse in the early days, the horse walking round in a mill which was geared onto the threshing machine. In later times the use of a steam engine was introduced, driving the machine with large leather belts. Contractors took their threshing machines from farm to farm, hauling them with a massive steam engine, and often pulling a caravan as well, to allow them to stay overnight.

The threshing machine was loaded from the top, the wheat dropped into a revolving drum with fixed wooden arms that beat the wheat seeds from the stalks. The seeds fell to the bottom and were sieved through into sacks. The remaining stalks were shaken to remove further grain, the remaining straw being ejected at the back.

There were a number of different manufacturers of threshing machines in Ayrshire. In Ayr J. & T. Young made them at their Vulcan Foundry. One of the larger manufacturers was George MacCartney & Co. of Cumnock. From 1812 he started redesigning the threshing mill. His first mill was used at Auchincross, near New Cumnock, where it proved to be a great success. At one time MacCartney's made one hundred threshing mills each year, selling at £80 each. They had made in excess of 1000 machines by 1912.

The threshing mill in the picture belonged to Andy Benson and is being used at Lochhill, near New Cumnock. In the foreground can be seen an old set of scales, used to weigh the filled sacks.

MAG 893

The First Combine Harvester at Dumfries House Estate

The threshing mill was replaced by the combine harvester, which arrived in Ayrshire in the late 1950s, quickly becoming more popular when manufacture of them commenced at Kilmarnock. This picture, which was taken around 1961-62, shows the first combine harvester used on Dumfries House Estate, hired in from a contractor. As can be seen in the picture, the farmers who worked on the estate were inquisitive of the new machine. The estate purchased its own combine harvester in 1963.

Early combine harvesters were built around tractors, and were virtually tractors with attached implements working in reverse. This one was an Allis Chalmers make, perhaps an All-Crop 100, and it had a bagger – the grain being sent up the chute and down into sacks. These filled sacks were kept on the combine harvester and then lowered down the chute on the left of the picture, around six or eight at a time. The combine is harvesting barley, which was taken away by the long-established firm of MacQuater Brothers of Maybole, grain merchants, and dried. Most of the barley was brought back to the farms and used for feed.

Combine harvesters were used to harvest grain from barley and wheat. The machine could cut the stalks and shake the grain from the heads, gathering the seeds in bags. The straw was left in lines on the fields, either to be gathered into stooks or baled. This was used for feeding in the winter months, or else for bedding.

The four men on the combine were (left to right), John Sharp, John Kirkland, Neil Ramsay and Hugh Porteous (Dumfries House Estate's farm foreman).

Neil Ramsay came with the combine from Mauchline contractors, Ramsay and Jackson, a business that was established soon after 1922 by William Ramsay, who commenced contract work with mobile threshing and baling machines, driven by steam traction engines. William Ramsay died in 1932 and James Jackson was brought in as a manager. In 1942 the business became Ramsay & Jackson and survives today as agricultural contractors.

Dung Spreader

The dung or manure produced in byres by cattle was gathered daily and piled up in the dung-midden, often located near to the byre. This dung was kept until the winter months, when it was taken from the midden and spread on the fields around the farm, encouraging the grass to grow. This took place in November through to March, depending on the weather and what sort of crop it was being applied for. Historically, the dung was taken in small quantities on a dung cart, drawn by a horse, and thrown by a worker using a type of fork with long tines, known locally as a graip, from the cart to the fields.

With the arrival of tractors, more mechanical dung-spreaders were developed, which could carry heavier loads and could also spread the dung more regular and further. One of the earlier manufacturers of dung spreaders was Alexander Jack & Sons of Maybole. This firm was founded in 1852 and by 1905 had 150 employees, making a variety of agricultural machinery. The firm could not, however, compete with larger makers of implements, and closed down in the 1960s.

The dung spreader shown here was a tractor drawn one, the tines and blades at the rear being turned by gears, throwing the dung from the trailer onto the fields. The amount of dung carried by the spreader was not great, and the farmer had to repeatedly return to the midden to refill it. Once the job was done, the spreader was washed, as Hugh Kirkland of Barmickhill farm is doing here, sometime in the 1960s. He has been using a Massey-Harris spreader.

Later spreaders were of the barrel type, a large cylindrical trailer opening at one side being filled with dung. A revolving bar in the central axis swung chains around, which threw the dung out the side. In more recent times, most of the dung is saved as slurry, and this is squirted onto the fields from slurry spreaders. Often these are now hired from contractors, the slurry sometimes being pumped by long lengths of pipe from the slurry tank onto the fields.

Pig Rearing

The breeding of pigs was at one time a major aspect of farming in Ayrshire, for the production of pork, but latterly more for bacon. Pigs were brought from Ireland and purchased by Ayrshire farmers. They were fed on the whey produced as a by-product of cheese making, fattening them for the market. The pig population of the county has dropped as follows – there were 15,452 in 1938, but only 9,461 in 1948. By the 1960s pig-breeding had virtually died out, one reason being the lack of whey produced as cheese-making was no longer carried out locally.

Writing in 1949, John Stevenson of Changue noted that 'the pig [in Ayrshire] has fallen on evil days. He is not now considered to be a fitting neighbour for the aristocratic Ayrshire cow, and so his numbers have been sadly depleted... The gladdening sight of a ham hanging from the kitchen rafters is now seldom ours, and only on rare occasions do we taste again the home cured porker's melting flesh.'

Ayrshire bacon became celebrated across the country. It has a distinctive flavour of its own, created by the method of manufacture. Unlike other curing processes, Ayrshire bacon was made from pigs whose skin and bones had been removed from the carcase. As a result, the curing process was both milder and quicker.

The processing of meat and pork has been carried out by a number of long-established firms across the county. Robert Wilson & Sons Ltd was established at a farm near to Dunlop in 1849 when he created what was one of the first bacon-curing factories in Scotland. The firm expanded for over a century, becoming famed for its Kennomeat and Cattomeat pet food, in addition to smoked ham, steak, beef, mince and luncheon meat.

Another long-established bacon-curer was Walter Mitchell of Ayr, founded in the nineteenth century. Their main factory was located off Main Street in Newton upon Ayr, but it was relocated to Heathfield as part of the redevelopment in the town centre in the 1960s.

The photograph was taken at Lowes farm, near New Cumnock, and shows Allan Young feeding his sow and piglets.

Newarkhill Farm

The steading at Newarkhill farm is typical of hundreds across Ayrshire. Located on a hill overlooking Ayr, within the estate of Newark Castle, the farmhouse is centrally placed with a byre to one side and a barn to the other. The only thing missing in this picture is a Dutch hayshed, usually painted red or sometimes green.

Most vernacular Ayrshire farms had a similar layout, a style that was developed in the early nineteenth century. Prior to this most farm buildings were smaller, often comprising only a single-storey thatched house with an adjoining byre. If one thinks of Burns' cottage at Alloway, it gives a good indication of what early farms were like.

In the eighteenth and nineteenth century the agricultural revolution resulted in many farms across the county being rebuilt. Estate owners were keen to improve their lands, and at this time many smaller holdings were merged into larger farms.

Most Ayrshire farms were part of larger estates, and for many years tenancies were offered on 19 year leases. In many cases, however, families were able to keep on their lease for longer, and some accounts relate how some families had tenanted the same farm for centuries. After the First World War many estates were broken up, or reduced in size, and it was around this time many farmers were able to become owners of their own farm for the first time.

Newarkhill was originally part of the Cassillis and Culzean estates, owned by the Kennedys. When this photograph was taken, perhaps in the mid 1930s, the farm was tenanted by Elizabeth Hutchison. The Hutchisons were able to purchase the farm at a later date. An older photograph of around 1860 exists, showing the house with a thatched roof.

Some estates built model farms, which were of a superior architectural standard, and which were thought to be more modern. A few examples were built across the county, such as Balgreen at Dalrymple, built on the Duke of Portland's Skeldon estate in 1882 to plans by the architect Robert Ingram, or else Lainshaw Mains farm, near Stewarton, a massive classical block of the early nineteenth century.

Townhead of Auchinleck Farm

Townhead farm was for centuries part of Auchinleck estate, owned by the Boswell family since 1504. The farmhouse, shown in this old photograph early in the twentieth century, is an example of the larger type of farmhouse that often was erected on Ayrshire farms. The open 'U' shaped steading is here laid out in a variation of the style, with the access road passing into the 'U' between the farmhouse and the barn.

Townhead as a farm probably only dates from around 1700, when the lands around Auchinleck House were improved. Prior to this, old maps do not show it, the farm of Kaillywhurn occupying the approximate vicinity. The famous diarist, James Boswell, who owned Auchinleck estate in the eighteenth century, visited Townhead on more than one occasion, though in May 1779 he noted that he viewed 'George Paton's dikes; not in good order.' Thomson's map of 1820 shows it as 'Tounhead', the Ayrshire pronunciation.

Auchinleck estate, like many across the country, was considerably reduced in size after the First World War. The whole estate of 12,000 acres was put up for sale in 1919, but there were no takers. Over the following years it was sold off farm by farm, often to the sitting tenants. Townhead farm was purchased by Bryce N. Sloan in 1921 for the sum of £3,500. With the same story repeated from estate to estate, thus, in the 1920s a considerable number of Ayrshire farms came into private ownership.

The Sloan family had been tenants on Townhead farm from 1798, the previous tenants being the Pedine, Peden or Paton family, probably all derivations of the same surname. John Sloan was born in 1851 at Townhead Farm, but moved to Creoch farm in New Cumnock parish in 1885, which he purchased from Dumfries House Estate around 1919. In 1912 he was part of Black Loch Curling Club rink that won the Eglinton Jug. He died in 1920. Today, the lands of Townhead extend to 180 acres and are owned by Gordon Sloan, grandson of Bryce.

Acknowledgments

I would like to thank a variety of people who have kindly supplied pictures that have been used in this book. They include Anne Cowan, Ian Crawford, Chris and Margaret Donaldson, Robert Guthrie, Daniel Hodge, Hugh Kirkland, John Kirkland, John McFadzean, Jimmy McGhee, Will and Marilyn Morton, David Raeside, Jan Shaw, Bill Sykes, James Templeton, Lorna Wardrop, Ben Welsh and Alastair and Mary Young. The other pictures are part of the author's own collection of images. I would also like to thank the many people who have supplied information to me over the years. Often these notes are filed away, to be used at some time in the future.